SMILE

SUP

Fingerlings™: ANNUAL 2019

A CENTUM BOOK 978-1-912564-98-9

Published in Great Britain by Centum Books Ltd

This edition published 2018

1 3 5 7 9 10 8 6 4 2

Fingerlings® and all product names, designations and logos are trademarks of WowWee Group Limited. Copyright 2016-2018 WowWee Group Limited. All rights reserved.

Centum Books Ltd, 20 Devon Square, Newton Abbot, Devon TQ12 2HR, UK

books@centumbooksltd.co.uk

CENTUM BOOKS Limited Reg. No. 07641486

A CIP catalogue record for this book is available from the British Library

Printed in Italy

YO

fingerlings™
friendship @ your fingertips

ANNUAL 2019

This book belongs to:

Ada

centum

CONTENTS

FUN, FRIENDSHIP AND ... FINGERLINGS!

Welcome to Melody Village, where the Fingerlings live.
It's a world full of colour, imagination and adventure,
where friendship is the most important thing of all.
Zoe, Boris and all their friends will be
so happy to hang out with you!

So swing into action and join your spirit animals for
some puzzle fun. Ready, set... **GO BANANAZ!**

There are 10 bananas hidden in this book.
Tick off a banana each time you spot one.
Can you find the whole bunch?

MEET THE MONKEYS (AND THEIR MATES!)

Zoe and her twin brother Boris have lots of friends. Trace the names and then use the dots to colour each cute creature.

Boris is a total chatterbox and he never. Stops. Talking.

Zoe

Boris

Gigi

Q. What is unicorn dandruff called?

A. Cornflakes!

Marge

8

Bella

Finn

Gemma

Kingsley

Mia

Sophie

9

VISIT THE VINES

Gigi has a gift for her monkey mate Zoe. Lead Gigi from Sparkle Heights to The Vines to deliver the lollipops.

START

FINISH

Q. What's the difference between a unicorn and a duck?

A. One goes quick and the other goes quack!

Answers on **page 76**

ODD UNICORN OUT

Unicorns are fun, fabulous and totally unique. Spot and circle the odd unicorn out in each row.

Gigi loves taking selfies! Every bit of her Crystal Penthouse is covered with photos of her and her friends.

1. a b c d e

2. a b c d e

3. a b c d e

4. a b c d e

Answers on page 76

HELLO, ZOE!

Zoe is always bright-eyed and full of energy. Read more about her here.

A group of monkeys is called a 'tribe', 'troop' or 'mission'.

NAME: Zoe

SPECIES: Monkey

HOME: The Vines

COLOUR COMBO: Turquoise and purple

LOVES: Reading *Unicornica* comics

" Zoe is my name and I love life upside down! "

THING I LIKE BEST ABOUT ZOE:

her shiny eyes

Zoe is my spirit animal:

YES ✓ NO ○

FUN WITH FINN

It's time to monkey around and have some fun with Finn!
How many times can you find the word 'FINN' in the grid,
and how many times can you find the word 'FUN'?

F	N	I	F
F	N	F	N	I
I	I	U	U	N
N	F	F	F	N
N	F	I	N	N

Answers on **page 76**

RECORD BREAKERS

Monkeys show how much they like other monkeys by grooming one another!

Zoe hopes to one day break the record for the most bounces in a single day, and go down in the *Fingerling Book Of Records*. Check out these amazing animal record breakers.

FACT: The sailfish is the world's fastest fish, and can swim at 68 miles an hour.

FACT: Mantis shrimp have the fastest punch of any animal.

FACT: The cheetah is the fastest land animal, running at more than 60 miles an hour.

FACT: The peregrine falcon is the fastest animal of all, and can fly at 200 miles an hour.

FACT: The blue whale is the largest and heaviest animal on Earth.

FACT: Giraffes are the tallest animals in the world.

HELLO, BORIS!

Boris is a music-loving monkey who is always on the move. Read more about him here.

Can you keep a secret? Boris still loves to hug his cuddly toy, Major Monkey. **Sssh!**

NAME: Boris

SPECIES: Monkey

HOME: The Vines

COLOUR COMBO: Blue and orange

LOVES: Cuddling his stuffed toy, Major Monkey

> " Boris is my name and laughter is my game! "

THING I LIKE BEST ABOUT BORIS:

~~their~~ he has a twin sister

Boris is my spirit animal:

YES ◯   NO ⊗

Q. What's a monkey's favourite thing to play on at the park?

A. The monkey bars!

COLOURFUL FRIENDS

Life is super-sweet for Gigi and Zoe.
Give the girls a little sprinkle of colour.

Q. What's the difference between a unicorn and a carrot?

A. One is a funny beast and the other is a bunny feast!

SECRET SLOTH

Marge has left a message for Kingsley. Help him work out what it says by circling every other letter. The first letter has been circled for you.

START

There are two types of sloths: the two-toed sloth and the three-toed sloth.

L A E S T K S S S S W M S U P R B F X

LET'S
SURF!

Answers on **page 76**

MONKEY MATCH

Pick a pal and play a swinging game of Monkey Match. It'll drive you bananaz!

Q. What do you call a monkey when it wins?

A. The chimp-ion!

HOW TO PLAY

- Have a good look at the monkeys on these pages, then cover each of them with a piece of paper.
- Take it in turns to pick up two pieces of paper, one from each page. If the monkeys underneath match, keep the pieces of paper. If they don't match, put the pieces of paper back.
- When all of the monkeys have been uncovered, the player with the most pieces of paper wins.

Monkeys can hold things things with both their hands and their feet.

Q. What do you call a
unicorn with no horn?

A. Pointless!

HAVE ○ WANT ○

HELLO, GIGI!

Gigi loves to swoosh her mane and snap a selfie. Read more about her here.

NAME: Gigi

SPECIES: Unicorn

HOME: Sparkle Heights

COLOUR COMBO: Cream, pink, blue and yellow

LOVES: Taking selfies

Feeling peckish in Sparkle Heights? Don't panic! Literally everything there is edible, even the weather. Cotton Candy clouds are deliciously light!

" Gigi is my name and I love chasing rainbows! "

THING I LIKE BEST ABOUT GIGI:

....

Gigi is my spirit animal:

YES ◯   NO ◯

23

PRETTY SHADOWS

Bella is a gymnast and she's got the moves. Draw a line to match each picture to the right shadow.

Q. What do monkeys wear when they are cooking?

A. Ape-rons!

Answers on **page 76**

COUNT THE CAKES

Gigi has topped her cakes with yummy gumdrops. How many of each colour cake from the box below can you count on the page?

Answers on **page 76**

DREAM HOUSE

Zoe's Bounce House is decorated with bubbles and Gigi's Crystal Penthouse is full of glitter and hearts. Design your own dream houses here.

What colours will you choose?

Zoe likes bouncing to pop music best of all!

This house is called:

....

What will you fill them with?

This house is called:

HELLO, MARGE!

Marge might speak slowly, but her mind is super-quick. Read more about her here.

NAME: Marge

SPECIES: Sloth

HOME: Sloth Beach

COLOUR COMBO: Light and dark purple

LOVES: Reading books

Fingerling sloths like to eat leaf tacos, topped with lots of bug sauce. **Yuck!**

> **My name is Marge and I love a good joke... even if it takes me a while to laugh!**

THING I LIKE BEST ABOUT MARGE:

Marge is my spirit animal:

YES ⬤   NO ⬤

Q. Why do sloths look forward to the end of the disco?

A. It's time for the slow dance!

GOING BANANAZ

Sophie is feeling hungry. Which path will lead her to the ripe, yellow banana?

Q. Why do gorillas have such big nostrils?

A. Because they have big fingers!

Answers on **page 76**

SLOTH SPEED

Marge is meeting her mates Finn and Boris in The Vines. Use the KEY to guide her through the grid and see how fast you can help the sloth move!

START

FINISH

KEY

Up

Left

Down

Right

Green algae grows on sloths' fur. It acts as camouflage, helping them blend into the tree.

Answers on page 76

RIDE AND RACE

START

FINISH

Q. What do sloths drink in the morning?

A. A cup of sloth-ee!

MEH

32

Marge and Kingsley are having a surfing competition. Race your friend by picking a path each to trace over with a pencil, without touching the sides. Who will reach the beach first?

START

Did you know, sloths can surf? Well, the ones who live in Melody Village can. **Far out!**

COOL

FINISH

33

TOP TALENTS

Boris has a hidden talent, he can eat a banana in one gulp! Find out what your friends' top talents are and write them here, along with yours.

My talent is:

....

My friends' talents are:

Name: .... Talent: ....

Name: .... Talent: ....

Name: .... Talent: ....

Name: .... Talent: ....

Name: .... Talent: ....

IT'S A TWIN THING

Zoe and Boris love hanging out together. Colour in the monkey twins.

HEYA

The Clubhouse is in a giant tree right in the centre of Melody Village. Zoe, Boris, Gigi and Marge hang out together there.

Hi

35

Q. How do monkeys get down the stairs?

A. They slide down the banana-ster!

HELLO, BELLA!

Bella is a super-cute monkey who is full of chatter. Read more about her here.

NAME: Bella

SPECIES: Monkey

HOME: The Vines

COLOUR COMBO: Pink and yellow

LOVES: Dancing and gymnastics

In The Clubhouse, the friends sometimes use tin cans to chat!

" Bella is my name and I express how I feel with cute monkey babble! "

THING I LIKE BEST ABOUT BELLA:

....

Bella is my spirit animal:

YES ◯   NO ◯

ALL ABOUT ADVENTURES

The Fingerlings love finding new places, making new friends and going on adventures. Plan your own adventure here.

I would go to:

....

....

We would pack:

....

....

I would go with:

....

....

We would get there by:

....

....

We would go to see:

....

FRONT

Draw a postcard picture.

HOLLA!

Boris is a clever impressionist – he can copy almost anyone's voice!

BACK

Message

Address

Q. Why did the monkey like the banana?

A. Because it had ap-peal!

39

FRIENDS 'N' PHOTOS

Gigi loves to pose for photos with her pals. Sketch or stick in some pictures of you and your friends to create a photo album.

OOPS!

Gigi once got stuck in the loo. It felt like she was in there for hours, but it was only six-and-a-half minutes!

Q. What do you call the cleverest unicorn in class?

A. An A-corn!

FEELIN' VINE

Bella, Sophie and Mia are hangin' around and having fun together. Which vine is the longest?

TIP: Place pieces of string along the vines, then use a ruler to measure each one.

START A

START B

START C

FINISH

FINISH

FINISH

Q. What did the banana do when he saw the monkey?

A. The banana split!

Answers on **page 77**

MONKEY BUSINESS

Hang around The Vines and you'll see the monkey mates. Give the gang some swingin' colours.

Zoe and Boris have a secret twin language. It's called Monkey Latin. When they use it, it's usually because they're bickering.

BELLA

FINN

BORIS

MIA

SOPHIE

ZOE

HELLO, FINN!

Finn likes to be different and swing out from the crowd. Read more about him here.

NAME: Finn

SPECIES: Monkey

HOME: The Vines

COLOUR COMBO: Black and blue

LOVES: Swinging around town

> " Finn is my name and I swing to the beat of my own drum! "

THING I LIKE BEST ABOUT FINN:

....

Finn is my spirit animal:

YES ⚪   NO ⚪

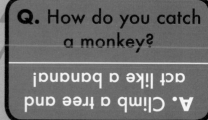

Q. How do you catch a monkey?

A. Climb a tree and act like a banana!

SURF'S UP

Marge and Kingsley love hangin' out at Sloth Beach and riding some waves. Design and colour a cool new surfboard for both sloths.

Thousands of years ago, sloths as big as elephants roamed Earth.

THUMBS UP

47

BELLA'S BUTTERFLIES

Bella has made some fluttery new friends. Draw pretty patterns on the butterfly wings and then add colour.

PLAYTIME

What do the monkeys want to play on today? Tick the word that best describes what each playground item is used for.

This is for:

The largest monkey in the world is the male **Mandrill** and the smallest is the **Pygmy Marmoset.**

◯ **Hanging**
◯ **Sliding**
◯ **Swinging**

This is for:

◯ **Hanging**
◯ **Sliding**
◯ **Swinging**

This is for:

◯ **Hanging**
◯ **Sliding**
◯ **Swinging**

SWING 'N' SPOT

Zoe, Boris and their monkey mates live in The Vines, the perfect place for swinging and singing. Can you spot 10 differences between the pictures below?

Monkeys living in The Vines like to wear ties. Why? Because there's nothing better than a monkey in a tie.

Colour in a banana each time you find a difference.

Q. Why did the monkey cross the road?

A. Because it was the chicken's day off!

Q. What did the baby unicorn
say to the mummy unicorn?

A. Where's my Popcorn?

HAVE 〇 WANT 〇

HELLO, GEMMA!

Gemma is always happy to pose for a photo.
Read more about her here.

In Sparkle Heights, the unicorns live like they're in a ballet. They dance and prance everywhere!

NAME: Gemma

SPECIES: Unicorn

HOME: Sparkle Heights

COLOUR COMBO: Pink, blue, white and yellow

LOVES: Anything glittery and sparkling

" My name is Gemma and I add sparkle to every day! "

THING I LIKE BEST ABOUT GEMMA:

....

Gemma is my spirit animal:

YES ◯   NO ◯

MONKEY MOVES

Bella is throwing a party for all of her Fingerling friends. It's time to practise your monkey moves before you swing onto the dance floor.

Monkeys can yawn, like humans. It might mean they are sleepy. Zzzzz!

YOU WILL NEED:
- 1 dice
- A dance partner (optional)

HOW TO PLAY

1. Take turns to roll the dice 10 times each, writing down every number rolled.

2. Each number on the dice matches a dance move. Write down the 10 dance moves you rolled.

3. Put on your favourite song and dance the moves. Keep repeating them until the song is over.

1 CLAP YOUR HANDS

2 HOP ON YOUR LEFT LEG

3 STAMP YOUR FEET

4 SPIN AROUND

5 WAVE YOUR HANDS

6 STAR JUMP

54

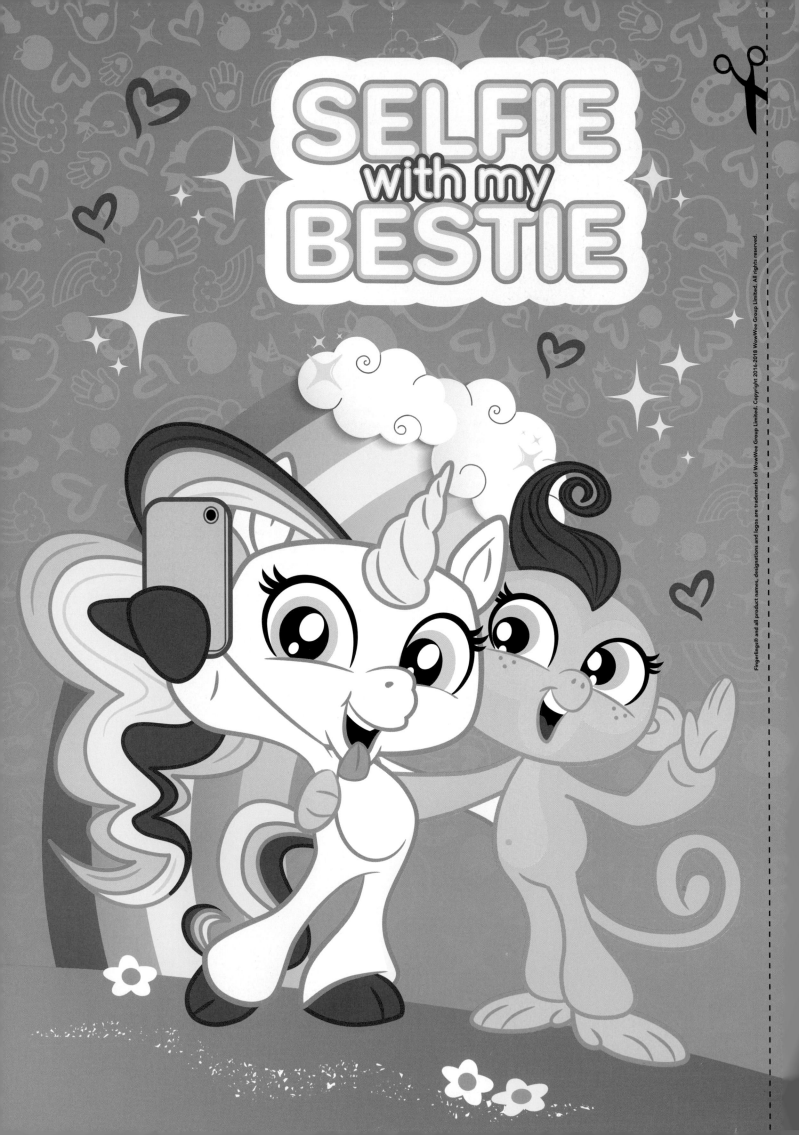

RAP STAR

Marge is a really good rapper. It's time to rhyme and write a new rap song for her to perform for her Fingerling fans.

Sometimes Marge is a bit slow and her fans clap before she's finished a song!

Song name: ....

....

....

....

....

....

....

....

HERE ARE SOME RHYMES TO INSPIRE YOU!

Surf / Turf   Hang / Bang   Slow / Grow
Friend / Bend   Book / Look   Vine / Shine

HELLO, KINGSLEY!

Kingsley is a laid-back surfer sloth. Read more about him here.

Sloths are actually great swimmers! They often drop from branches into the water.

NAME: Kingsley

SPECIES: Sloth

HOME: Sloth Beach

COLOUR COMBO: Light and dark

LOVES: Surfing

> " Kingsley is my name... slow and silly is my claim to fame. "

THING I LIKE BEST ABOUT KINGSLEY:

Kingsley is my spirit animal:

YES ◯   NO ◯

HAVE ◯ WANT ◯

Q. What type of berries do sloths love to eat?

A. Sloe berries!

MARGE'S MAPS

Marge's room at Sloth Tree House is covered in maps. Draw a new one for her to hang up, showing the place you live. Make sure you put your house on the map!

Marge once found a treasure map and it lead to ... a recipe for leaf coleslaw!

Q. What do you do with a sloth when you've washed it?

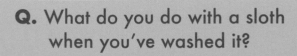

A. Hang it on the washing line!

Things you could draw:
- School
- The park
- Your BFF's house

JUST CHILLIN'

Sloths are always super-chilled. Add some cool colours to Kingsley and Marge.

Q. What do sloths write in Valentine's cards?

A. I love you slow much!

UP IN THE AIR

Zoe is swinging high in the sky where the weather is fine. Draw the missing pictures to complete this puzzle.

Zoe is full of energy and she's always on the move. So it's just as well she lives in a bouncy house!

There should be one of each picture in every row across, column down and mini grid.

Q. What did the banana say to the monkey?

A. Nothing – bananas can't talk!

HAVE ◯ WANT ◯

64

HELLO, MIA!

Mia is curious and is always asking questions. Read more about her here.

Monkeys have unique fingerprints, just like humans do.

NAME: Mia

SPECIES: Monkey

HOME: The Vines

COLOUR COMBO: Purple and white

LOVES: Exploring and new adventures

> 66 Mia is my name and I'm interested in the giant world around me! 99

THING I LIKE BEST ABOUT MIA:

Mia is my spirit animal:

YES ◯ NO ◯

SILLY SLOTH

As well as rapping, Marge enjoys making everyone laugh. She knows lots of jokes, but it can take her a while to tell each one!

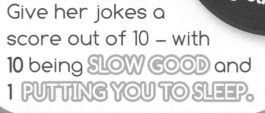

Sloths usually only leave the treetops once a week week... to go to the toilet on the ground!

Give her jokes a score out of 10 – with 10 being **SLOW GOOD** and 1 **PUTTING YOU TO SLEEP.**

Q What do sloths throw in winter?

A Slowballs!   OUT OF **10**

Q What did the boy sloth say to the girl sloth?

A I'd like to hang out with you!   OUT OF **10**

Q What do you call a sloth that likes to be the centre of attention

A A slow-off!   OUT OF **10**

Q What is a sloth's favourite type of party?

A A slumber party!   OUT OF **10**

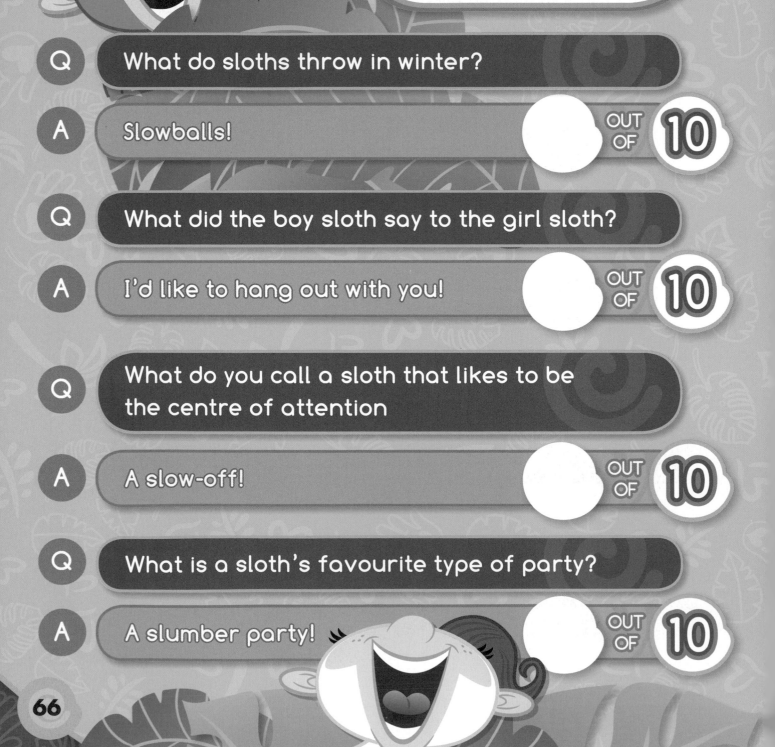

Q. What is a sloth's favourite way to travel?

A. On a slow coach!

Q What do sloths make when it snows?

A Slow angels! OUT OF 10

Q Why do sloths make bad racing drivers?

A He'd stick to the slow lane! OUT OF 10

Q What do sloths like to read?

A Snooze-papers! OUT OF 10

Q What is a sloth's favourite time of the day?

A Nap time! OUT OF 10

Q What do sloths like to watch on TV?

A Game slows! OUT OF 10

Q What motto do sloths live by?

A Don't hurry, be happy! OUT OF 10

WHO'S HIDING?

The monkeys are playing hide-and-seek around The Vines. Can you work out which monkey from the box below is hiding in each tree?

Bella   Boris   Mia   Zoe   Finn   Sophie

Answers on **page 77**

DREAM DAY

Zoe's perfect day starts with a healthy breakfast and some jumpy jumps at the park, followed by a crazy adventure with her friends. Describe your dream day here.

Zoe's secret dream? To become a superhero like comic-book star Unicornica.

Morning: ....

....

....

....

....

Afternoon: ....

....

....

....

....

Evening: ....

....

....

....

HELLO, SOPHIE!

Sophie can always be called on for a cuddle. Read more about her here.

Everything in the The Vines is banana-themed, which is really ap-peal-ing to the monkeys who live there!

NAME: Sophie

SPECIES: Monkey

HOME: The Vines

COLOUR COMBO: White and pink

LOVES: Blowing kisses

> " Sophie is my name and I am full of loving hugs! "

THING I LIKE BEST ABOUT SOPHIE: hugs hug

Sophie is my spirit animal:

YES ◯   NO ◯

HAVE ◯ WANT ◯

Q. What do you call a baby monkey that's just like its dad?

A. A chimp off the old block!

71

FUN AT YOUR FINGERTIPS

Ask an adult to help you.

Remove the finger puppet pages and scenes at the back of the book and colour in the Fingerlings. Stick the pages on thin card and cut out the Fingerlings, finger tabs, scenes and stands. Slot them together, then take each character on all sorts of **BANANAZ ADVENTURES** with you! Here are suggestions for three fun things you could do...

Strike A Pose

Q. What does a unicorn wear in her mane?

A. A rain-bow!

Take a selfie with Gemma and Gigi. Practise posing with your unicorn pals, and maybe mix it up with some monkey and sloth group shots.

Become An Explorer

Explore the world around you. Use your imagination to turn a flower bed into an exotic jungle or a chair into a mountain to climb.

Build A Home

Find some empty cardboard boxes and turn them into Melody Village homes. From Zoe's Bounce House to Gigi's Crystal Penthouse, every Fingerling's home is as special as they are!

THE NAME GAME

How well do you know the creatures who live in Melody Village? Look at the faces below and then write their names into the boxes.

Spider monkeys get their name because of their long arms, legs and tail.

Answers on **page 77**

GIGI'S JIGSAW

With lollipops and cupcakes galore, Sparkle Heights is Gigi and Gemma's taste-tastic home. Can you complete the jigsaw by matching the pieces to the spaces?

1

2

3

4

5

6

a

b

c

d

e

f

Q. What did the unicorn have to wear at school?

A. A uni-form!

Answers on page 77

ANSWERS

The hidden bananas can be found on page 9, page 19, page 24, page 30, page 43, page 49, page 54, page 63, page 68 and page 75.

PAGE 10

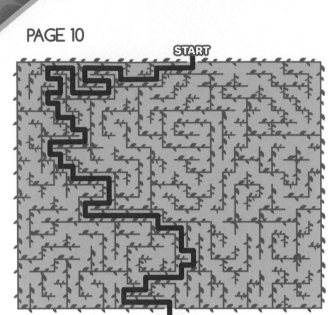

PAGE 11

1 – b ,
2 – e,
3 – a,
4 – c.

PAGE 14

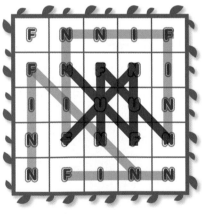

Finn = 6, Fun = 5.

PAGE 19

LET'S SURF!

PAGE 24

PAGE 25

PAGE 30

Path B.

PAGE 31

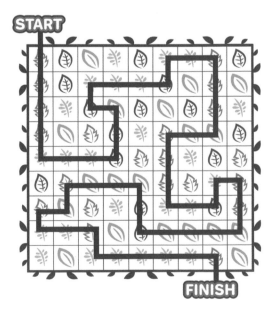

PAGE 42

Vine c is the longest.

PAGE 49

 is for hanging.

 is for swinging.

 is for swinging.

PAGES 50-51

PAGE 63

PAGE 68

a – Finn,

b – Sophie,

c – Bella,

d – Mia,

e – Boris,

f – Zoe.

PAGE 74

PAGE 75

1 – b, 2 – f, 3 – d, 4 – e, 5 – a, 6 – c.

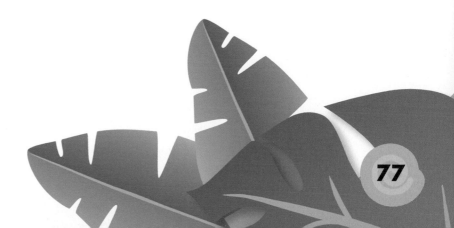

FINGERLINGS™
friendship @ your fingertips

Gigi

GLUE HERE

Finger Tab

Finger Tab

GLUE HERE

FINGERLINGS™
friendship @ your fingertips

Gemma

Kingsley

GLUE HERE

Finger Tab

FINGERLINGS™
friendship @ your fingertips

Finger Tab

GLUE HERE

Marge

FINGERLINGS™
friendship @ your fingertips

Mia

Finger Tab

GLUE HERE

Finger Tab

GLUE HERE

FINGERLINGS™
friendship @ your fingertips

SOPHIE

Line up the slots in the play scene with the slots in the stands, and then fix together.

B

B

B

FINGERLINGS™
friendship @ your fingertips

Zoe

GLUE HERE

Finger Tab

Finger Tab

GLUE HERE

BORIS

FINGERLINGS™
friendship @ your fingertips

Line up the slots in the play scene with the slots in the stands, and then fix together.

Line up the slots in the play scene with the slots in the stands, and then fix together.